Going Shopping

Building Bridges Series

Building Bridges Series: Going Shopping
Text by Catherine White
Illustrations by Marta Kwasniewska
Copyright © Gatehouse Media Limited 2017

First published and distributed in 2017 by Gatehouse Media Limited

ISBN: 978-1-84231-177-6

British Library Cataloguing-in-Publication Data:
A catalogue record for this book is available from the British Library

Jamal and his friend, Ali, meet in town.

They are going to look round the shops.

They go into an old record shop.

Jamal likes to look at the record sleeves.

He likes to look at the artwork.

He dreams of being a great artist.

Ali likes listening to the music.

He dreams of playing in a band.

He dreams of being a famous drummer.

In his dream, fans scream with joy

when the band plays.

Jamal and Ali spend a long time

in the old record shop.

The shopkeeper is getting cross.

He can tell they are not going

to buy anything!

Next, they go to the computer shop.

They go inside to see all the latest gadgets.

They look at tablets and laptops.

They look at PCs and TVs.

They look at mobile phones and cameras.

Jamal and Ali spend a long time
in the computer shop.
The shop assistant is getting cross.
She can tell they are not going
to buy anything!

Afterwards, they find a café.
They are thirsty and hungry.
They order a drink and some food
from the lady at the counter.

"What can I get for you?" the lady asks
with a smile.

"A Coke and a slice of cake, please,"
says Jamal.

"I'd like a cup of coffee and
a cheese sandwich," says Ali.

"Go and sit down," the lady says.
"I'll bring it over to you."

The café is busy.

They find a table and sit down.

While they wait, they talk about all the things
they have seen in the shops.

They talk about all the gadgets
they would like to buy.

Jamal wants to buy a laptop.
Ali wants to buy a new mobile phone.

"We need to find a good job with good pay,"
says Jamal.

Ali says, "Perhaps we can get a job
in the computer shop."

"What a good idea," says Jamal.
"Maybe we'll get a staff discount, too,"
he says. "Let's try."

If you have enjoyed this book, why not try another title in the *Building Bridges Series:*

Going to College
Finding a Home
Getting a Job
Meeting Friends
Seeing the Doctor

Gatehouse Books®

Gatehouse Books are written for older teenagers and adults who are developing their basic reading and writing or English language skills.

The format of our books is clear and uncluttered.
The language is familiar and the text is often line-broken, so that each line ends at a natural pause.

Gatehouse Books are widely used within Adult Basic Education throughout the English speaking world.
They are also a valuable resource within the Prison Education Service and Probation Services, Social Services and secondary schools - in both basic skills and ESOL teaching.

Catalogue available

Gatehouse Media Limited
PO Box 965
Warrington
WA4 9DE

Tel/Fax: 01925 267778
E-mail: info@gatehousebooks.com
Website: www.gatehousebooks.com